THE UDDERLY MOOVELLOUS JOKE BOOK

Steve Cole

Illustrated by Woody Fox

RED FOX

THE UDDERLY MOOVELLOUS JOKE BOOK
A RED FOX BOOK 978 1 862 30882 4

First published in Great Britain by Red Fox,
an imprint of Random House Children's Books
A Random House Group Company

This edition published 2009

1 3 5 7 9 10 8 6 4 2

Text copyright © Steve Cole, 2009
Illustrations copyright © Woody Fox, 2009

Set in Bembo Schoolbook

Red Fox Books are published by Random House Children's Books,
61–63 Uxbridge Road, London W5 5SA

www.kidsatrandomhouse.co.uk
www.rbooks.co.uk
Addresses for companies within
The Random House Group Limited can be found at:
www.randomhouse.co.uk/offices.htm

THE RANDOM HOUSE GROUP Limited Reg. No. 954009

A CIP catalogue record for this book is available from the British Library.

Printed in the UK by
CPI Bookmarque, Croydon CR0 4TD

To Tobey, Nathan, Cassie and Amy

★ THE C.I.A. FILES ★

Cows from the present —
Fighting in the past to protect the future . . .

In the year 2550, after thousands of years of being eaten and milked, cows finally live as equals with humans in their own country of Luckyburger. But a group of evil war-loving bulls — the Fed-up Bull Institute — is not satisfied.

Using time machines and deadly ter-moo-nator agents, the F.B.I. is trying to change Earth's history. These bulls plan to enslave all humans and put savage cows in charge of the planet. Their actions threaten to plunge all cowkind into cruel and cowardly chaos . . .

The C.I.A. was set up to stop them.

However, the best agents come not from 2550 — but from the past. From a time in the early 21st century, when the first clever cows began to appear. A time when a brainy bull named Angus McMoo invented the first time machine, little realizing he would soon become the F.B.I.'s number one enemy . . .

TOP SECRET FILES —
COWS OF COURAGE . . .
AND COMEDY

McMoo and his young friends Pat and Bo are star agents of the C.I.A. – short for COWS IN ACTION! These super-tough cow-mandos travel through time in a converted cowshed, fighting evil cattle from the future and keeping history on the right track . . .

PROFESSOR ANGUS MCMO
Type of cattle: Bull
Character: Inventive, ingenious, quick-thinking, tea-drinking hero
Favourite Joke: Why is the letter *F* like a cow's tail?
Because it's always on the end of beef.

LITTLE BO VINE
Type of cattle: Milk cow
Character: Tough, cheeky, fashionable rebel cow
Favourite Joke: How can you tell if a cow is a mugger? *She'll be wearing a balaclava in a dark alley.*

PAT VINE
Type of cattle: Bullock
Character: Brave, loyal, determined sidekick
Favourite Joke: Do you know how long cows should be milked? *The same as short ones*

ENEMY AGENT: T808
Type of cattle: Ter-moo-nator
Character: Part robot, part bull, all horrible
Favourite Joke: Joke? What is joke? Malfunction! Joke does not compute!

Prof. McMoo's
TIMELINE OF NOTABLE
HISTORICAL EVENTS

13.7 billion years BC

BIG BANG - UNIVERSE BEGINS

(and first tea atoms created)

4.6 billion years BC

PLANET EARTH FORMS

(good job too)

23 million years BC

FIRST COWS APPEAR

(23 million is my lucky number!)

1700 BC

SHEN NUNG MAKES FIRST CUP OF TEA

(what a hero!)

7000 BC

FIRST CATTLE KEPT ON FARMS

(Not a great year for cows)

1901 AD

QUEEN VICTORIA DIES

(she was not a-moo-sed)

2550 BC

GREAT PYRAMID BUILT AT GIZA

(by an Egyptian geezer)

31 BC
ROMAN EMPIRE FOUNDED

(Roam-Moo empire founded by a cow but no one remembers that)

1509 AD
HENRY VIII COMES TO THE THRONE

(and probably squashes it)

1066 AD
BATTLE OF HASTINGS

(but what about the Cattle of Hastings?)

1620 AD
ENGLISH PILGRIMS SETTLE IN AMERICA

(bringing with them the first cows to moo in an American accent)

1939 AD
WORLD WAR TWO BEGINS

(or World War Moo as it is known to cows)

2007 AD
I INVENT A TIME MACHINE!!!

2500 AD
COW NATION OF LUCKYBURGER FOUNDED

(HOORAY!)

(about time!)

2550 AD
COWS IN ACTION RECRUIT PROFESSOR McMOO, PAT AND BO

(and now the fun REALLY starts...)

1903 AD
FIRST TEABAGS INVENTED

THE UDDERLY MOOVELLOUS JOKE BOOK

Introduction

A FUNNY MISSION

An ear-bursting alarm was ringing through the Time Shed. Professor McMoo bustled about the controls, flicking switches and pulling levers. His friends, Pat and Bo, watched him anxiously.

"What a racket!" Bo complained, sticking bubblegum in her ears.

"Is it the C.I.A. calling us from the future?" asked Pat.

"It certainly is," McMoo agreed. "Director Yak is sending a top-secret message straight to our computer, so the information can't be stolen by evil bulls."

"What do you call a bull who steals things?" Bo grinned. **"A beef-burglar!"**

Pat groaned. But the professor shushed them both as the alarm went quiet and the image of Yak – a hairy black bull – appeared on the computer screen.

"Red alert, troops," said Yak. "Our spies report that a ter-moo-nator is on the loose, hunting down the funniest joke of all time. A joke so hilarious it could make people die laughing!"

McMoo gasped. "With a joke like that they could cause havoc throughout history!"

Pat nodded. "Imagine if they told it to a prime minister or a president about to make a vital speech . . . Or an army about to start a major battle . . ."

"As evil weapons go, I guess you can't knock a killer joke," said Bo.

"Unless it's a *knock-knock* joke, of course," McMoo put in. "Where is this ter-moo-nator now?"

"We don't know," Yak admitted. "What we do know is that his name is T808. He was kicked out of the zoo last week for feeding the squirrels."

Bo shrugged. "Doesn't sound so bad."

"He was feeding them to the lions," said Yak gravely. "Anyway, our spies report that T808 is going to be looking for the joke in a particular place — a place where you three have battled and beaten a ter-moo-nator in the past. You must track down that joke before he does and put him off the scent. Take care, troops. Yak out."

The screen went blank.

"Somewhere that we've battled and beaten a ter-moo-nator in the past . . ." mused Pat.

Bo nodded. "Sounds like we'll have to return to the scenes of all our old adventures and get searching."

"We must gather all the jokes we can too," McMoo declared. "If T808 has already found that joke, we must be able to defend ourselves! But first, to get us in the mood . . . **Knock! Knock!**"

Bo frowned. *"Who's there?"*

"Philip!"

"*Philip who?*"

"Philip my bucket with tea, could you?" McMoo winked at her. "I'm parched!"

Chapter One

COMIC COWS!

"Maybe we should start our search right here on the farm," Pat suggested. "After all, we met our very first ter-moo-nator in this shed."

"True," said Bo. "And since cows
are the funniest animals ever in the
history of the world ever, ever, EVER,
we should start grabbing all the **cow
jokes** we can!"

"Computer!" called McMoo. "Give us
the cow-joke file . . ."

Have you heard about
the idiot who found three
milk bottles in a field?
He thought it was a cow's nest.

What do cows eat for breakfast?
Moo-sli.

What game do cows play at parties?
Moo-sical chairs.

What would happen
if cows could fly?
The price of beef would go up.

Knock, knock.
Who's there?
Lass.
Lass who?
Lass who that cow now!

Where would you find a prehistoric cow?
In a moo-seum.

What goes "oom, oom"?
A cow walking backwards.

What is cowhide most used for?
Holding cows together.

What's black and
white and red all over?
A cow with sunburn.

Where would you find
a cow with no legs?
Where you left it.
And what do you **call**
a cow with no legs?
Ground beef.

Knock, knock.
Who's there?
Cows go.
Cows go who?
No they don't, they go "moo".

If milk comes from a cow, where does wine come from?
A wine-oceros.

What do you get if you cross a cocoa bean with a cow?
A chocolate moo-se.

Where do cows go on holiday?
Moojorca.

What did the bull sing to the cow?
"When I fall in love . . . it will be for heifer."

Knock! Knock!
Who's there?
The interrupting cow!
The interrupting—?
MOOOOOOOO!

Where do cows
go when they
want a night out?
The moooovies.

What do you
call a bull asleep
on the ground?
A bulldozer.

How do you count a herd of cows?
With a cow-culator.

What do you call a cow
in an earthquake?
A milkshake!

Where does a cow live?
On the udder street.

Which is more nourishing,
a cow or a shooting star?
A shooting star, because it is meteor.

What do you call a cow
spying on another cow?
A steak-out.

What do you call a cow that
can't give milk?
An udder failure!

Why don't cows have any money?
Because people milk them dry.

Why don't most cows wear bells?
Two horns are enough warning!

Why did the bull rush?
Because it saw the cowslip!

What theatre shows make cows feel ill?
Moo-sickals!

What's got horns, udders
and cuts grass?
A lawnmooer.

Why did the dairy worker take
the cows to the top of the
hill to milk them?
*Because he heard the cream
rises at the top.*

What do you get if you cross a cow,
a sheep and a baby goat?
The milky baa kid.

What do you get if you cross
a cow with an octopus?
*I don't know — but
at least it can milk itself.*

What do you get if you
cross a cow pat with
a boomerang?
*A nasty smell that
keeps coming back!*

How do you hire a cow?
Put it on stilts!

What do you
get if you
cross a cow
with a camel?
*Lumpy
milkshakes!*

What do you get if you
cross a coal mine with a cow?
A pit-bull.

Why did the farmer send his
cows to the gym twice a week?
He wanted low-fat milk.

What's the difference
between apples and cowpats?
*If you don't know, I'm never going
to ask you to bake a pie!*

How do you stop
milk from turning sour?
Leave it inside the cow!

What was the first animal in space?
The cow who jumped over the moon.

And why did he
jump over the moon?
He forgot where he left his spaceship!

Chapter Two

FUNNY FARMYARD!

"Those cow jokes weren't bad," McMoo reflected. "But to be on the safe side, perhaps we should gather some gags about the whole farmyard."

"The whole farmyard?" Pat gulped. "Even gags about . . . Bessie Barmer?" Bessie was the farmer's wife, a mean monster of a woman. She hated all the farm animals and longed to turn them into pies.

"Why not?" McMoo smiled. "If you laugh at scary things, it makes them less frightening . . ."

"I've got some!" Bo cried.

**Why did Bessie spend the day
stomping up and down in her field?**
She wanted to grow mashed potatoes!

Why did Bessie stick razors
in the potato patch?
She wanted to grow chips!

Why did Bessie call her pig Ink?
Because he kept running out of the pen!

And why did Ink keep running?
Because Bessie took him for grunted!

**What happened when
Bessie took up the piano?**
She hurt her back!

Why did Farmer Barmer tell
Bessie to walk ten miles a day?
*So in a month's time,
she'd be 300 miles away!*

**Why didn't Bessie Barmer
go water-skiing?**
She couldn't find a lake with a slope on it!

What's big, fat and smells?
Bessie Barmer's bum!

"All right, Bo, that's quite enough about Bessie," said Professor McMoo with a smile. "Do you know any chicken jokes?"

"What do you think I am," Bo grumbled. "**A comedi-hen?**"

"I know some chicken jokes," said Pat excitedly. "In fact, I know quite a few farmyard gags . . ."

What kind of bird lays electric eggs?
A battery hen!

What goes: Peck, BANG! Peck,
BANG! Peck, BANG!?
A bunch of chickens in a field full of balloons!

**What do you get if you feed
gunpowder to a chicken?**
An egg-splosion!

Why did the unwashed
chicken cross the road twice?
Because he was a dirty double-crosser!

**How do you cure a
chicken with chicken pox?**
Give her some henicillin!

What do you get from
a Scottish chicken?
Scotch eggs!

Why does a chicken watch TV?
For hentertainment!

Why did the chicken
want to join the band?
Because it had its own drumsticks!

If a rooster lays an egg
on top of a pointed roof,
which way will it roll down?
Roosters do not lay eggs!

What kind of tie does a pig wear?
A pig's tie!

Why did Bo Peep lose her sheep?
She had a crook with her!

What is a horse's favourite sport?
Stable tennis!

**Why was the lamb
told off for being rude?**
He wouldn't say "thank ewe" to his mum!

Why did the ram fall over the cliff?
He didn't see the ewe turn!

Why did the pig go to the casino?
To play the slop machine!

What is the opposite of
cock-a-doodle-doo?
Cock-a-doodle-don't!

How do roosters know when to crow?
They set an alarm cluck!

What do you give a pony with a cold?
Cough stirrup!

How do you change a pumpkin into another vegetable?
You throw it up in the air and it comes down SQUASH!

What do you call a tall
building full of pigs?
A sty-scraper!

How do sheep
keep warm in the winter?
Central bleating!

"Is that the best you can do, little
bruv?" Bo grinned. "It's **laugh-a-bull**!"

McMoo was chortling to himself. "I
love farmyard jokes," he said. "But I
think it's time we went back in time to
hunt for this moo-sterious killer joke."
He pulled a big red lever. The Time Shed
clanked and quivered as it started to shift
away through time.

"I hope it won't make *us* die
laughing," said Pat nervously.

"I've never heard of a joke *that* funny,"
McMoo confessed. "But T808 must be
certain it exists to embark on this
mission into history."

"Maybe he's **embarking mad**!" Bo grinned. "Anyway — where shall we start looking?"

"I've got an idea," said McMoo. "Let's ask 'mummy' . . . !"

Chapter Three

EGYPTIAN EJOKES!

"Here's the plan," said Professor McMoo. "We'll search for T808 through history, starting with our earliest F.B.I. battle and working our way forwards. So – first stop, ancient Egypt! The fourth of September 1250 BC, to be precise."

"That means we've just got rid of that rubbish old *moo-my* who was trying to trash history," Bo realized. "Tutankha-moooo!"

In a matter of minutes the Time Shed had arrived with a resounding thud on the desert sands.

"How will we find T808, Professor?" asked Pat nervously.

29

"I've got a time-tech scanner – it will scan for any technology that doesn't belong in this time," said McMoo.

"I hope we find him quickly." Bo knocked her hooves together. "I've got a hoof sandwich that will knock the smile right off that ter-moo-nator's ugly face."

"First, let's put a smile on our own faces," said McMoo. "I happen to know a lot of jokes about ancient Egypt."

"Are the jokes ancient too?" Pat asked innocently.

"Fairly!" McMoo beamed. "Judge for yourself . . ."

**Why did the mummy leave
his tomb after 1,000 years?**
*Because he thought he
was old enough to leave home!*

Why was the Egyptian girl confused?
Because her daddy was a mummy.

**How do you use an Egyptian
mummy's doorbell?**
Toot-and-come-in!

What do you call an Egyptian
hula-hoop covered in fluff?
A pharaoh's fur-O!

**What do you call a bandaged
figure with an enormous bottom?**
A bummy mummy!

What do you call a bandaged
figure with no teeth?
A gummy mummy!

What do you call a bandaged figure dipped in melted chocolate and cream?
A yummy mummy!

What do you call a bandaged figure that's just blown up?
Gross!

Where do mummies go for a swim?
To the Dead Sea!

Why was the mummy so tense?
He was all wound up!

Why do mummies never tell secrets?
Because they keep everything under wraps!

What is a mummy's favourite type of music?
Wrap!

How do you find Tutankhamun's tomb?
Peer–amid the other tombs!

What was the final score at the pharaoh's football match?
One–nile!

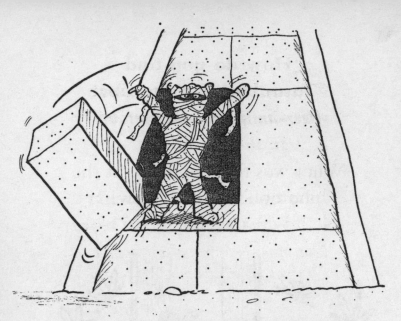

What's the difference between a man who won't have books in his house and a mummy?
One has banned pages, the other has band-ages!

What kind of girl does a mummy take on a date?
Any old girl he can dig up!

What is the speed limit in Egypt?
50 Niles per hour.

**Whereabouts in his tomb
was the pharaoh buried?**
In the pyramiddle!

What's the difference between a
pyramid and a really good bloke?
*Not much – one's a top geezer,
and the other's atop Ghiza!*

**Why did the mummy
cobra have to stay at
home with her kids?**
She couldn't find a baby-spitter.

Where does Tutankhamun
put his spare change?
In his mummy box.

**What do you call a
mummy in a rocket?**
Tutankha-moon.

**What do you call a
noble Egyptian mummy?**
Sir Cophagus.

What was the mummy's curse?
*BIG FAT PHARAOH BOTTOMS, I
JUST BANGED MY TOE!*

"OK, Professor, that's enough!" cried Pat, holding his sides. "Some of those jokes are truly terrible."

McMoo grinned. "Thanks, Pat!"

"But is there any sign of the ter-moo-nator?" Bo enquired.

The professor scanned his instruments. "Nothing. Looks like we're in the wrong place at the wrong time."

"Perhaps T808 hasn't turned up yet," Pat suggested. "That would make him a **ter-moo-*later*!**"

Bo winced. "Quick, Prof, let's split for our next destination – before Pat the **cow-median** here tells any more awful jokes!"

Chapter Four

NO PLACE LIKE ROME!

Before you could say "**Gladiator couple of sandwiches before I came out**", the Time Shed was appearing in ancient Rome in a haze of purple light.

"It's the year AD64," McMoo announced to Pat and Bo. "We met crazy Emperor Nero last time we were here — perhaps we could ask him if he knows any good gags."

"Emperor Zero was a full-time nut," said Bo flatly. "And I'm going to *do* my nut if we don't find T808 soon. I really hope he's *Rome-ing* about somewhere . . ."

"The time-tech scanner will soon tell us," said McMoo, flicking some switches. "You know, the ancient Romans were

quite fond of jokes and riddles. Here's one they got off the ancient Greeks, first written around 429 BC."

Question: Which animals walk on four feet in the morning, two at midday and three in the evening?
Answer: Human beings. They move on all fours as babies, on two feet as adults and use a cane in old age.

"That's total pants!" cried Bo. "Babies don't have four feet! And how can a cane be a foot?"

"It could be a foot *long*!" Pat suggested.

"Pah!" said Bo. "In any case, T808 will have to hunt a bit harder for his killer joke if that's the best these toga-wearing types can come up with!"

"And while we're hunting for him," said McMoo, "let's pass the time with some rather better Roman jokes from the computer files. Computer . . . ?"

Where is Hadrian's Wall?
Around Hadrian's garden!

What was the greatest accomplishment
of the early Romans?
Speaking Latin!

What is a forum?
Two-um plus two-um!

BO: When was Rome built, Pat?
PAT: At night.
BO: How can you be sure?
PAT: The professor's always saying Rome wasn't built in a day!

How was the Roman
Empire cut in half?
With a pair of Caesars!

Who were the hottest fighters in Rome?
The gladi-radiators!

Who succeeded the first
Emperor of Rome?
The second one!

What do you say to get
Romans joining in?
All toga-ther now!

What happened when the slave
put his head into a lion's mouth
to count how many teeth he had?
*The lion closed its mouth to see how
many heads the slave had!*

Did the ancient Romans hunt bear?
Not in the winter!

Why did the Romans build
straight roads?
So their soldiers didn't go round the bend!

Which Roman emperor was the coolest?
Julius Freezer!

Which Roman emperor drank fifty
litres of orange juice a day?
Julius Squeezer!

Which Roman emperor kept
a mouse on his head?
Julius Cheeser!

Which Roman emperor was
full of the joys of spring?
Julius Geyser!

Which Roman emperor was
always on the toilet?
Poo-lius Wee-zer!

Did Roman citizens
enjoy large markets?
Yes, they were all for-um!

What do you call a Roman
emperor who has adventures?
An action Nero!

McMOO: What is the time?
NERO: XX past VII!

The flow of jokes was cut off by a loud
ping from the time-tech scanner.

"Another no-show," said Pat nervously.
"Where *is* that ter-moo-nator?"

"Plenty of possibilities left," McMoo reminded him, tweaking the Time Shed's controls. "Let's jump forward five hundred years or so to the time of King Arthur . . ."

"We'd better bring our torches then!" Bo told him. "It'll be **knight-time**!"

Chapter Five

JOKING ALL KNIGHT!

"There we are then," cried McMoo as the Time Shed crashed to a juddering halt. "Sixth-century England – the Dark Ages."

"We'll soon brighten up the place!"
Bo declared. "Come on, let's see how
King Arthur and Merlin are getting on
since we saw them last."

McMoo put a restraining hoof on her
shoulder. "Before we go barging in like
bulls in an England shop, let's see if my
time-tech scanner can find any trace of
T808 . . ." He flicked a switch and the
scanner started whirring.

"I can't believe we met all those real
knights," said Pat dreamily. "I overheard

the court jester when I was in Cow-
melot that evening. He told loads of
top jokes ..."

Bo nodded eagerly. "Come on then —
now you can tell them to us!"

**What do you call a knight
who is afraid to fight?**
Sir Render.

What time is it when a knight
looks at his belly button?
The middle of the knight!

What helps a knight get to sleep?
His knight-light!

What does a knight wear to bed?
His knightie.

What game did King Arthur play?
Knights and crosses!

What do you call a
mosquito in a tin suit?
A bite in shining armour!

**Why were the early days of
history called the Dark Ages?**
Because there were so many knights!

What did the dragon say
when he saw Sir Lancelot?
"Oh, no! Not more tinned food!"

**Why did King Arthur
have a round table?**
So no one could corner him!

Which one of King Arthur's knights
got a big boil on his bottom?
Sir Lanced-a-lot!

**Who came up with the
idea of a round table?**
Sir Cumference!

Why did King Arthur put
his jester on his head?
*He mixed up his loyal clown
with his royal crown!*

**Where do knights
learn to kill dragons?**
At knight school!

Why did King Arthur put an enormous
cup of tea on top of Merlin?
Because he knew Merlin was a great saucerer!

There are many castles in
the world, but who is strong
enough to move one?
Any chess player!

What did Sir Lancelot's mother
say to him at bedtime?
Knighty-knight!

Where will you find the most
modern homes for knights?
In New-castle!

Where did King Arthur
go for entertainment?
To a knight club!

How do you interrupt a knight?
"Joust a minute . . . !"

Did you know most of King
Arthur's men had trouble sleeping?
It was one sleepless knight after another!

When a knight in armour was killed in battle, what was written on his grave?

Rust in peace!

**What early king of England
was famous for writing
books at his round table?**
King Author!

What type of musical instrument
did the early Britons play?
The Anglo-Saxophone.

**Why did the knight run about
shouting for a tin opener?**
He had a wasp in his suit of armour!

What is the difference between a
knight and Santa's reindeer?
*One slays the dragon and the
other's draggin' the sleigh!*

Pat's jokes were interrupted by the
mournful BEEP! of the time-tech
scanner, finding nothing out of place in
the land outside the shed.

"So T808 isn't looking for the joke in
this time, either," McMoo muttered.

"It's just *knight* fair!" Bo
complained. "I really want to clobber
him!"

"You remind me of history, Bo,"
said Pat. **"You're
always repeating
yourself!"**

"Am I?" said Bo.
"Yes," Pat said.
"Am I?" said Bo.
"That's enough,
you two!" McMoo

had turned back to the Time Shed's controls. "That last joke of yours, Pat, about the knight and Santa's reindeer – it reminds me of another of our adventures . . ."

"Of course!" Pat cried. "And with all the ho, ho, ho-ing going on at that time of year, the jokes should be funnier than ever!"

Chapter Six

JOKES TO *SLEIGH* YOU!

The Time Shed reappeared on a snowy December day in 1066.

"Happy Christmoos!" said McMoo.

"It was only happy once we beat up Moodolph the red-nosed ter-moo-nator," Bo reminded him. "But if you want to

give me a present, you can let me beat up T808 too!"

"Just be glad the Battle of Hastings is over," Pat told her.

"Was that the famous conflict between cows and bees?" asked Bo. "Oh, no – that was the *Cattle of Hay-Stings*!"

"Ooof!" said Pat. "Come on, let's see if we have any luck with the time-tech scanner here."

McMoo nodded and set the machine going. "Of course, the fantastic thing about a time machine is that it really can be Christmas every day! Let's have a big cup of tea to celebrate . . ." He went over to a big bale of straw – and gasped. "Hey!"

"No, it's definitely straw," said Bo.

McMoo shot her a look, then picked up a huge box. "Look – Christmas crackers! Daisy Micklepud, the Christmas-crazy cow, must have left them behind before going back to the C.I.A."

"Let's pull them!" Pat urged him. "There'll be a joke inside each one."

"It'll pass the time till we find what's waiting *out*side," Bo agreed, tearing open the box and pulling the first cracker . . .

Have you heard the one about the giant Christmas cake?
It's very hard to swallow.

Which Christmas carol is
popular in the desert?
"O cam—el ye faithful . . . !"

**How did Jack Frost fall
and scrape his knees?**
He was doing wheelies on his icicle!

What did the lumberjack
do before Christmas?
He went on a chopping spree!

**What do you get if you cross
a witch with a snowstorm?**
A cold spell!

What happens when you
slip on thin ice?
You get a THAW butt!

**What do you sing at
a snowman's birthday party?**
FREEZE a jolly good fellow!

Who is never hungry at Christmas?
A turkey – it's always stuffed!

What do you call an old snowman?
Water!

What goes: Now you see me, now you don't, now you see me, now you don't?
Santa's beard on a zebra crossing!

What's white and goes up?
A stupid snowflake!

Knock
knock!
Who's there?
Snow.
Snow who?
Snow use –
I've forgotten
my name
again!

**When does Christmas
come before Easter?**
In the dictionary!

What do you get in December that
you can't get in any other month?
The letter D!

**What's impossible to
overtake at Christmas?**
The three wide men!

How does Good King
Wenceslas like his pizzas?
Deep and crisp and even!

How does a snowman lose weight?
He waits for the temperature to rise!

What did one snowman say
to the other snowman?
Can you smell carrots?

What do you get when you cross
a snowman with a vampire?
Frostbite!

What did the mixed-up
baker give Santa Claws?
A loaf of white beard!

How many presents can
Santa fit in an empty sack?
Only one – after that it's
not empty any more!

Who hides in the bakery at Christmas?
A mince spy!

What do you get if you eat
Christmas decorations?
Tinselitus!

Where do snowmen go to dance?
A snow ball!

Who delivers presents to baby sharks at Christmas?
Santa Jaws!

What do you get if you cross an apple
with a Christmas tree?
A pineapple!

**What kind of candle burns longer,
a red candle or a green candle?**
Neither — candles always burn shorter!

Did you hear about the man arrested
for stealing a calendar at Christmas?
He got twelve months!

**Why are Christmas trees terrible at
sewing?**
They drop so many needles!

What falls at the North Pole but never
gets hurt?
Snow!

**What falls at the North Pole and
does get hurt?**
Santa toppling off the chimney!

What falls at the North Pole, *does* get hurt and then blows up?
Santa toppling off the chimney and landing on a bomb!

What do you call a glowing Santa suit floating in the sky?
A U.F.Ho-ho-ho!

What is the best Christmas present in the world?
A broken drum – you can't beat it!

What swings around the jungle and tastes like Christmas cake?
Tarzipan.

What do you get if you cross a duck
with Santa?
A Christmas quacker.

**What runs through the jungle at
Christmas shouting "Ho ho ho"?**
A Santa-lope.

Why was the fairy on the
Christmas tree cross?
*How would YOU like having
a Christmas tree stuck up
your bottom for three weeks?*

Pat, Bo and the professor chuckled
heartily at that one. But then the time-
tech scanner pinged again to say that
nothing out of place was spoiling this
ancient English Christmas.

"From ho-ho-ho to no-no-no,"
McMoo reflected. "But I'm sure we'll
find T808 presently."

"Just not **Christmas presently**!" Pat agreed.

"It's time for a Happy New Year," McMoo announced as the Time Shed clanked and rattled onwards into the future. "Almost five centuries after the last one . . ."

Chapter Seven

ROYAL HOWLERS!

In no time at all, the C.I.A. agents were all in a *new* time. "We're still in England," McMoo reported. "In the grounds of Hampton Court Palace in January 1540."

Bo grinned. "That's where we sorted out that ter-moo-nator who was trying to get rid of Henry the Eighth . . ."

"Tudor times!" Pat exclaimed, then his stomach gurgled. "How I wish I could **chew da** grass!"

"First things first, Pat," said McMoo. "The Tudors have something in common with our mission in this time . . . Both start with a T – one with the letter T, one with a *cup* of tea!" He chuckled.

"Meantime, I'll scan again for any sign of old steel-chops . . ."

"Professor," said Bo curiously, "what was the first joke ever told?"

"Oh, it was back in the Stone Age sometime," said McMoo. "It went: **'Ug, ug, ooh? Ohh-ah-ah-FNURRRR!'**"

"You're making it up," Bo complained.

"True," said McMoo. "But I can tell you the earliest one-liner recorded in Britain.

It's from a 'jest book' written in the year 1526 . . ."

When a boy was asked by the Law to say his father's craft, the boy answered that his father was a crafty man of Law.

"That's rubbish." Bo blew a gum-bubble. "The only way that joke could

kill someone is by boring them to death!"

"Olden but not golden," Pat agreed, putting tea bags in the pot. "For brainboxes only!"

"Which reminds me," said McMoo. **"There's one word that is usually pronounced wrongly, even by brainboxes."**

"Oh, yeah?" Bo raised her eyebrows. **"Which word is that?"**

"'Wrongly'!" McMoo replied, smiling as his young friends groaned.

"Wait a minute!" Bo was peeking out of the shed doors. **"Who's that lady up the ladder in front of the palace, wearing a crown?"**

McMoo crossed to see. "Who, her? **That's just the window queen-er!"**

He laughed. "Now, while we're waiting for the kettle to boil and the time-tech scan to finish . . . Computer? Give us the royal joke file!"

Where are kings and queens
usually crowned?
On the head!

What did Henry the Eighth do
when he burped?
He issued a royal pardon!

How did Henry the Eighth
dress on a cold day?
Quickly!

What was Henry the Eighth's
middle name?
The.

What did Henry the Eighth
get for Christmas?
Fat.

Why did Henry the Eighth
have so many wives?
He liked to chop and change.

What did Anne Boleyn's mum
say when her daughter confessed
she loved Henry the Eighth?
*That man's not worth
losing your head over.*

Why is Henry the Eighth like
part of the postal service?
Because he's a royal male.

Why did Henry the Eighth
go to the dentist?
To get his teeth crowned!

What do you call it when
a king goes to the bathroom?
A royal flush!

When is a piece of wood,
plastic or metal like
a king or queen?
When it's a ruler!

HENRY VIII: Did you know I can lift an elephant with one hand!
McMOO: I've never seen a one-handed elephant, Henry!

What's a king's favourite clothing?
A reign-coat!

Why did the overweight
king put glue in his food?
He wanted to stick to his diet!

What do you call a fight
in a chocolate factory?
The War of the Roses!

Which gorilla had six wives?
Henry the Ape!

What did Henry the Eighth
do to the evil chicken?
He ordered her eggs-ecuted!

What did Queen Victoria
say when she stepped
in a cowpat?
We are not a-moo-sed!

"Well, I am *very* a-moo-sed," McMoo chuckled, slurping the tea Pat passed to him as his time-tech scanner gave its familiar *ping*. "But there's no sign of a ter-moo-nator out there in 1540. History is just as it should be."

"Boring!" Bo complained.

"So, where next?" asked Pat.

"To a place where we can really make a splash . . ." McMoo drained his tea and busied himself at the Time Shed's controls. "And we'll get there by hook or by nautical crook – *me hearties*!"

Chapter Eight

HA-HARRRRRRRRR!

The Time Shed landed upon the soft white sands of a tropical island.

"Here we are then," said McMoo. "The Caribbean Sea, 1718 – in the very waters that Moobeard the pirate once sailed."

"And Blackbeard too," Pat reminded him. "Those pirates were ever so fierce and smelly – but we'd never have beaten Moobeard without them!"

"**My earrings came from an American pirate, you know,**" said Bo. "**They cost me a buccaneer!** A buck an ear – get it?"

McMoo chortled. "I'm afraid I do." He switched on the time-tech scanner. "But will we get T808 this time?"

"There's nothing but sea out there." Pat sighed. "*Water* place to have to search!"

 "And *water* perfect opportunity to strike gold with some potty pirate puns and riddles while we're waiting!" McMoo told him. "Ha-HARRRRRR! Get a load of these . . ."

How do you make a pirate cross?
Take off the p and he becomes irate!

Which pirate had the biggest hat?
The one with the biggest head!

What happened to the shipwrecked pirate who had to live on a tin of pilchards for a fortnight?
He kept falling off!

When is a boat like a heap of snow?
When it's adrift.

**What do you call a happy
pirate with one leg?**
A hop-timist!

How did Moobeard get rid of
the man with a wooden leg?
He told him to hop it!

**Why didn't Blackbeard
believe what the sardine said?**
Because it sounded fishy!

Why did the fish blush?
Because it saw the ocean's bottom!

Have you heard the ocean's roar?
Well, it's not likely to be cooked, is it?

Why wouldn't Blackbeard
touch the ship's log?
He kept getting splinters!

Where did Blackbeard keep his money?
In a sand bank.

Why do pirates carry swords?
Because swords can't walk.

**Why should you never
listen to a pirate in bed?**
Because he's lying.

Where does a sick ship go?
To the dock!

**What's the difference between a
fisherman and a fed-up librarian?**
*One baits his hooks,
the other hates his books!*

What's higher than an admiral?
An admiral's hat!

When is a ship not a ship?
When it turns into a harbour!

When is a sailor like a plank of wood?
When he's aboard!

Why are dolphins clever?
They swim in schools!

Why are
pirates so strong?
*Because they
hold up ships!*

**Which pirate
had a parrot
that shouted,
"Pieces of four!"?**
Short John Silver!

**BLACKBEARD:
You remind
me of the sea.**
BESSIE:
Because I'm
wild, deep
and inviting?
**BLACKBEARD:
No, because
you make
me feel sick.**

What happened to the ship
that sank in a pool of piranhas?
It returned with a skeleton crew!

What do you call a baby crab?
A little nipper!

What happened when the lazy
pirate rested on the plank?
He soon dropped off!

What type of house weighs the least?
A lighthouse!

What's the hardest thing about
learning to climb the rigging?
The deck!

How do you get a shellfish up a cliff?
Oyster up!

What part of a fish weighs the most?
The scales!

**How does a pirate
octopus go into battle?**
Well armed!

How do you help a deaf pirate?
Give him a herring aid!

What kind of pirate never steals?
A dead pirate!

What's a pirate's least
favourite vegetable?
A leek!

**Why did Blackbeard
buy some birdseed?**
He wanted to grow himself a parrot!

Why couldn't the pirate play cards?
He was sitting on the deck!

**What's got very sharp teeth and
lives at the end of the rainbow?**
A croc of gold!

Why did Blackbeard leave a chicken
where he buried his treasure?
Because eggs marked the spot!

But then the time-tech machine
pinged away again, and Bo stamped her
foot with frustration. "Looks like we're
not going to find that ter-moo-nator in
1718, either!"

"I can **sea-weed** better leave!"
quipped McMoo, working some more
levers. "But with every place we cross off
our list, we're getting closer to a
showdown."

Pat nodded. "I suppose it's time to
moo-sey on through time to the
joketastic site of our Wild West
showdown with the F.B.I. . . ."

Chapter Nine

YEEEEEEE-HA-HA-HA-HA!

"Here we are," cried McMoo as the Time Shed clattered to a halt in the plains of the old American West. "It's the year 1875. This is where we beat Ter-moo-nator T-65 and his friends when they tried to buy up all the land they could get their hooves on . . ."

Suddenly the time-tech scanner started beeping urgently.

Pat and Bo gasped.

"There's something out there on the range that doesn't belong in this time," McMoo told them.

"It must be T–808!" Bo realized. "Let's get out there and wallop him!"

"Perhaps we should get some gags together first," said Pat nervously. "So if he's already found the deadly joke, we can fight back."

"Good thinking, Pat," said McMoo. "I know quite a few about the old Wild West. Try these for starters . . ."

**Why can't a ranch-hand
with no cattle complain?**
He's got no beef!

A cowboy rode to an inn on Friday.
He stayed two nights and left on
Friday. How could that be?
His horse was called Friday!

**Why was the horse
so gloomy?**
It was wearing a sad-dle!

Why did the cowboy ride
a yacht across his range?
He thought it would be plains sailing!

**What is the difference between
a horse and the weather?**
One is reined up, the other rains down!

Why did the cowboy go to the rodeo?
To get a few bucks!

**Why did the cowboy fold
over every dollar note he owned?**
He wanted to double his money!

Why did the horse cross the road?
To visit his neigh-bour!

**Have you heard about the
cowboy who was thrown
through a wall by his horse?**
He's said to be in a stable condition!

What did the cowboy say when his
girl asked him to whisper something
soft and mushy in her ear?
"Fresh-laid cowpats!"

**What do you call the
horse that runs the city?**
The mare!

What did the horse say when he fell?
"I've fallen and I can't giddy-up!"

**What kind of horses go
out after dark?**
Nightmares!

Why was the cowboy a lot of laughs?
He was always horsing around!

Why are cowboys like cartoonists?
They both have to learn to draw fast!

Why did the cowboy die
with his boots on?
*Because he didn't want to stub
his toe when he kicked the bucket.*

**Why did the cowboy
put his bed in the fire?**
So that he could sleep like a log!

What kind of cowboy steals teapots?
A kettle rustler!

**What's extinct and
worked in rodeos?**
A bronco-saurus!

Do cowboys ever shoo the flies
that buzz around their horses?
No, they let them go barefoot!

**Why did the cowboy get
a burning hot butt?**
He was always riding the range!

Knock! Knock!
Who's there?
Moscow.
Moscow who?
Moscow is black and pa's cow is brown
with white spots!

**What has three heads,
one hat, two arms, two wings,
eight legs and two tails?**
A cowboy on a horse carrying a falcon!

"OK, Professor, that's enough!" Bo ran
to the shed doors. "Let's just get out
there and clobber him!"

"Careful, Bo," McMoo commanded.
"According to the scanner, the out-of–
time technology is lurking right
outside!"

"Not for long!" Bo cried. "I'll splatter
it!" She kicked open the door, dived
through the air – and landed in a very

large, very fresh cowpat that exploded
everywhere!

"Ugh!" Pat turned up his nose. "You
certainly splattered something!"

Several oxen had been standing about
outside, and now they hurried away
from Bo in surprise. But there was no
sign of T808 anywhere. Bo pulled a face
and held up a mucky metal circuit to
the professor. "Is this what your dumb
scanner picked up?"

"Bless my horns!" said McMoo, carefully taking the smelly component. "It seems to be a broken bit from a butter bazooka." He threw it into the Time Shed, and the scanner stopped bleeping. "Hmm. There's nothing else out here that's from the wrong time."

Pat nodded. "That bit of butter bazooka must have been dropped by one of those F.B.I. agents that used to patrol the plains – **beef-ore** we stopped them!"

"AND WE SHALL HAVE REVENGE!" droned a deep metallic voice from the back of the shed.

McMoo, Pat and Bo whirled round in amazement.

There, stepping out from behind the costume cupboard at the back of the Time Shed, was Ter-moo-nator T808!

Chapter Ten

TER-MOO-NATOR TICKLERS!

Bo peered at T808. "I never forget someone I've drenched in milk and kicked," she said. "You're the very first ter-moo-nator we ever met, right here in this shed."

T808 nodded. "Correct."

"Of course," said McMoo gravely. "Yak's agents knew you'd gone to a place where we'd once defeated a ter-moo-nator. But none of us realized you'd sneaked on board the Time Shed itself!"

"I arrived here in secret while you spoke to your dire Director," T808 explained smugly. "You defeated me once, when I was T178, and made me a laughing stock among other ter-moo-nators. Now, in my new identity, I shall prove I'm better than anyone – by making you laugh all the way to your doom!"

Pat frowned. "But how could you hope to find this deadly joke of yours just hiding in the back of the shed?"

"Simple," grated the ter-moo-nator. "I have recorded every one of the jokes YOU have told today. I have analysed your laughter at each. Now I shall combine and condense the best jokes into one SUPER-joke, powerful enough to destroy anyone who hears it!"

Bo frowned. "But . . . jokes don't work that way, tin-head!"

"Silence," snapped T808. "You shall become my super-joke's first victims." He cleared his throat with an electronic cough, paused impressively and then . . .

What did knock in the who king moo the pirate before mummy cow Nero chicken?

He cough a bottom curse,
his knight hen in a bandaged
sea bum milkshake!

Professor McMoo, Pat and Bo looked at him blankly.

"Why are you not dying of laughter?" asked T808 crossly.

"Perhaps it's the way you tell them," said Pat.

"Or perhaps it's 'cause your joke  made less sense than a prawn in pants!" Bo added.

"I'm afraid you've sent yourself on a fool's errand, T808," said McMoo, his eyes bright.

"Silly jokes aren't harmful to humans, only to ter-moo-nators – because you can't get your miserable metal minds around the idea of a good laugh."

"You lie!" T808 grated.

"We'll see about that," said Bo. "**What do you get if you sit under a cow?**"

"Um . . ." The ter-moo-nator's horns trembled slightly. "Shelter when it is raining?"

"No, dummy – you get a *pat on the head*!"

"Not funny," roared T808. "Organic waste may clog vital circuits!"

"**What's the difference between a ter-moo-nator and a biscuit?**" Pat demanded. "**You can't dip a ter-moo-nator in your tea!**"

"Illogical," T808 groaned, a wisp of steam escaping his snout as he raised a ray gun. "A biscuit is a small disc of sweetened dough, while a ter-moo-nator is a highly advanced part-organic robot—"

"– with no imagination," cried
McMoo triumphantly. "His data banks
are so stuffed with crazy jokes it's
starting to scramble his metal mind. We
must tell him some quick-fire jokes –
before he fires that gun!"

Pat and Bo didn't need telling
twice . . .

**Did you hear about the
ter-moo-nator who came away
from the bird show with first prize?**
He ate the winning parrot!

Can a ter-moo-nator jump
higher than a bus?
Yes — buses can't jump!

**How do you make
a ter-moo-nator float?**
*Pour cola over your favourite ice
cream and add a ter-moo-nator!*

Why do ter-moo-nators in
a hot-air balloon never argue?
They don't want to fall out!

What's the difference between a ter-moo-nator in the twenty-fifth century and one in the twenty-first?
About 400 years!

What do you get if you cross
a bulldog with a ter-moo-nator?
A burger that bites back!

What do you call a good-looking, friendly ter-moo-nator?
A failure!

What's a ter-moo-nator's favourite drink?
Punch!

What would you get if you crossed
a parrot with a ter-moo-nator?
*I don't know, but if it wanted
a cracker, you'd better give it one!*

What happened to the
ter-moo-nator who fell
into a cement mixer?
He became a hardened criminal!

What do you get if you cross
a ter-moo-nator with a cockerel?
A tin of roost beef!

By now, T808 was staggering about
with smoke pouring from his joints,
sparks buzzing around his robotic head.
"Joke overload . . . Nonsense filters
failing . . . Cannot compute . . ."

"One more joke ought to finish him
off!" cried McMoo.

"Leave it to me," said Pat.

Knock! Knock!
Who's there?
Howard.
Howard who?
**How 'ard can it be
to defeat a ter-moo-nator?**

"Ha!" Bo yelled. "Not hard at all
when you've got jokes like those!"
"Mission abort," wailed T808,

pulling a silver plate from behind his back and staggering onto it. "Cannot compute . . . mission abort . . ."

"You're the biggest joke of all, techno-chops!" yelled Bo – as T808 faded away in a cloud of black smoke.

"Whew," said McMoo. "That's him taken care of."

"And Yak will be pleased," Pat added. "We stopped that ter-moo-nator's loopy plan – even if it would never have worked."

"It was our jokes that defeated him in the end," said McMoo. "Let's hope they never start making ter-moo-nators with a funny bone."

"Doubt it," said Bo. "They'll make them with proper tools like they normally do!"

Pat groaned, Bo struck a victory pose, and Professor McMoo smiled and steered the Time Shed back home . . .

McMoo: Knock! Knock!
Pat: Who's there?
McMoo: Abyssinia!
Bo: Abyssinia who?
McMoo: Abyssinia in the next exciting C.I.A. adventure – and I can't wait!

THE END

THE TER-MOO-NATORS
by Steve Cole

IT'S 'UDDER' MADNESS!

Genius cow Professor McMoo and his trusty sidekicks, Pat and Bo, are the star agents of the C.I.A. – short for COWS IN ACTION! They travel through time, fighting evil bulls from the future and keeping history on the right track . . .

When Professor McMoo invents a brilliant TIME MACHINE, he and his friends are soon attacked by a terrifying TER-MOO-NATOR – a deadly robo-cow who wants to mess with the past and change the future! And that's only the start of an incredible ADVENTURE that takes McMoo, Pat and Bo from a cow paradise in the future to the SCARY dungeons of King Henry VIII . . .

It's time for action. COWS IN ACTION

ISBN: 978 1 862 30189 4

THE PIRATE MOO-TINY
by Steve Cole

OX MARKS THE SPOT!

Genius cow Professor McMoo and his trusty sidekicks, Pat and Bo, are star agents of the C.I.A. – short for COWS IN ACTION! They travel through time, fighting evil bulls from the future and keeping history on the right track . . .

In 1978, robotic danger HAUNTS the seven seas . . . Posing as a pirate, a TER-MOO-NATOR is capturing ships in the Caribbean. But why? And what terrible treasure is he hiding on SPOOKY Udderdoom Island? McMoo, Pat and Bo set sail on a big, BUCCANEERING adventure to find answers before pirate BULLS takes over the world . . .

It's time for action. COWS IN ACTION

ISBN: 978 1 862 30541 0